11/20

D1597663

The A, B, C's of Plum Island, Massachusetts
A Sampling of the Past and Present

SAVING CREW—PLUM ISLAND, NEWBURYPORT, MASS.

By Jenn Bogard
Descendant of Plum Island Lighthouse Keeper, Arthur W. Woods, Sr.

Special Thanks:

Friends of Plum Island Light

Susan Boccuzzo
Tom Holbrook, of RiverRun Bookstore and Piscataqua Press

Parker River National Wildlife Refuge
Friends of Parker River National Wildlife Refuge
Massachusetts Marine Fisheries Shellfish Purification Plant and Peter Kimball
Surfland Bait and Tackle
Steve Atherton, Board of Directors and Charter Member of Friends of Plum Island Light
Craig Filmore
Denise LaCroix
Ted Olsson, President of the Friends of Parker River National Wildlife Refuge
Nancy Pau, Wildlife Biologist, Parker River National Wildlife Refuge
Dana Pederson
Matt Poole
Janet Woodman

Arthur and Barbara Woods, grandparents
Family and friends who weighed in on the cover
Rob Bogard
Tiffany Woods Boccuzzo
Brittany Williams

Photography Credits:

Steve Atherton
Letters B, E (aerial view)
Aerial photos taken during PITA sponsored flight

Jennifer and Eric Humphrey
harborbeachphotography.com
harborbeachphotography@gmail.com
Letters A, E (sand dune) H, I (boardwalk), J, L (close-up of lens),
M (weathered shop & The Pink House), P (sign),Q, R, T, Z Back Cover

Matt Poole, U.S. Fish and Wildlife Service
Letters N, P (all birds), U

U.S. Fish and Wildlife Service
Letter I (Beach Plum Shrub)

Brenda Lusher
Letter X

Jenn Bogard
Letters C, F

Shutterstock
Letter S, Front Cover

Depositphotos
Letters W, Y

Black and White photo of original two towers (letter L) reprinted with permission from the Friends of Plum Island Light

The ABC's of Plum Island, Massachusetts
Copyright 2018 by Jenn Bogard
All Rights Reserved

Published by Piscataqua Press
32 Daniel St., Portsmouth NH 03801
www.ppressbooks.com

ISBN: 978-1-944393-81-6

"For Arthur and Barbara Woods, for their love of the Island"

Dear Readers,

Many of the poems in this book are "found poems." One way to write found poetry is by picking words or phrases from texts around you such as signs, blogs, books, maps, videos, etc. then reshaping these words into a poem. Readers like to know where you found the words and phrases, so be sure to tell them. Check out the last page in this book to see where I found words for my poems.

This book is a celebration of Plum Island, Massachusetts.

Airfield

Go for a ride in a 'Flying Machine'

New England's first flying field, 1910

Barrier island

Barrier island
Fragile and narrow

Protecting the mainland
Absorbing the force
Of the ocean and storms

Clams

Soft shelled clams
Clean themselves
At the Shellfish Purification Plant
Just by breathing in
And feeding in
Clean seawater

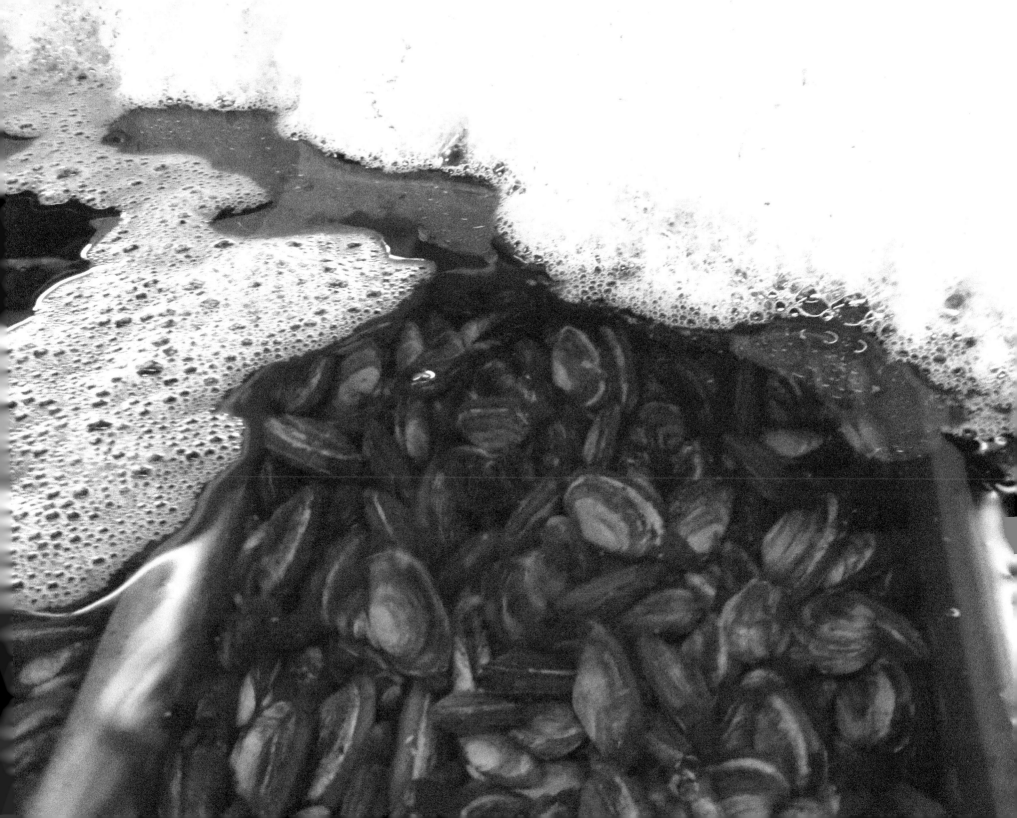

Lunch.

Sunday
Feb 26th Nice day.
Art went up to the
Station after the paper
also went up to Daniels.
Ben got
L. Dogwood

Monday
Children went to
School in the morning
walked home in the
afternoon. Made a
Chocolate cake.
Good night.

Tuesday
Feb 21st Nice day. Children
went to School colder.
blowing.

Wednesday
Washingtons
Birthday. Cloudy
snowed in the morning
Grace came

Wednesday
March 1st nice day
blowing quite a breeze.
Helen and I walked to
Town and for
Grace and

March 2nd

Thursday
Feb 23rd
Children
Par walked
hard

Feb 24th
morning. nice
blowing. Child
to School. Went
Hoosic's in the

Saturday
Feb 25th
Lovely day jus
Spring. The
Art and

is washing away and I am not
sorry.

Sunday
Feb 5th
Good day Par went went
up to the Station after the paper.

Monday
Feb 6th cold and raw cloudy
looks like a storm. Par went to
Town with the Captain and got a
few things Art went over I should
say up to meet him. Par went
over and fixed the range lights
today. Finished my skirt ruffle
today.

Tuesday
Feb 7th
this is an awful day snowing and
blowing a gale. Fuller was in the
evening

Diary 1911

Diary of a Plum Island Lighthouse Keeper and his family

Dear Diary,

I must tell you about
The weather
The winds
Who went to school when
And visits with people
On the island

Erosion

Water
Rushing
Winds
Whipping

Storms
Moving
The sand

Over time

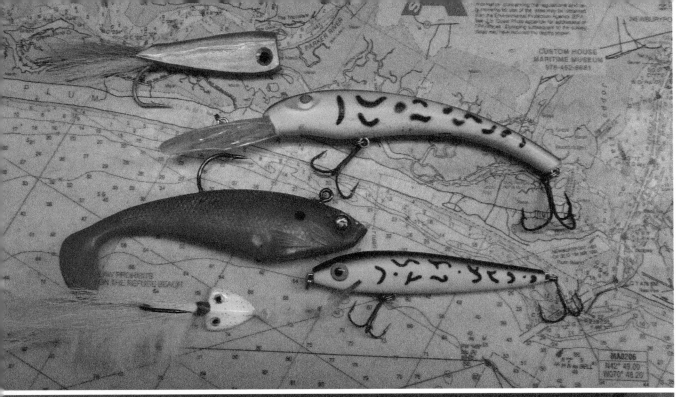

Fishing

Fish for flounder
Fish for striper
Catch a blue fish
Catch a cod

Pictured from long ago: Myrtle
England with a tuna fish she caught off
Plum Island

Grace

Look into my eyes
I'm Grace
I took charge of
The Light
For my father
In times of need

E. Grace Woods was the daughter of Arthur W. Woods, Sr., Keeper of Newburyport Harbor from August 25, 1905 until his death, August 30, 1919.

Hellcat tower and trail

Birdlife
in the trees

and in the
thickets

In the marsh shallows
and in the sky

Climb high
and look

Stay quiet
and listen

Indigenous plant

Beach Plum
Shrubs
Grow in the
Sand dunes
And give
Plum Island
Its name

Jump in!

Jump in
Go for a swim
The water is
Cold
At first

Keepers of the light

Faithful watchings
Day and night

Superhuman efforts
To save life

Sept. 7. 1917
Plum Island Light Station.
Newburyport Mass.
Receive from Arthur W. Woods.
$ 100.00 one hundred dollars for Caring for the
Range Lights at Salisbury Beach from Nov. 7. 1916
to Sept. 7. 1917.
Received Payment in full
× Carl Barck.

Aug. 7. 1918
Plum Island Light
Newburyport Mass.
Received from Arthur W. Woode
$.20.00 twenty dollars for takeing
Care of Range Lights at Salisbury
Beach from June 7. 1918 to
Aug 7. 1918,
Received Payment in full
William H Pearce

Lighthouse
Plum Island/Newburyport Harbor Light

Ships traveled the coast
From lighthouse to lighthouse
And I guided them
Into the Merrimack River
With the beams of my light

From time to time,

Newburyport, Mass. - Plum Island Light

the lighthouses had to be moved

to different locations on Plum Island!

Mysterious buildings

Can you see through
The sands of time?
Back to when a boatbuilder
Crafted wooden boats
In a neat little workshop
On the bank of Plum Bush Creek

Boatbuilder forced to close shop

By Barry Cardigan, Globe Staff

The sands of time were already running out on well - designed and artfully constructed row boats — "pulling boats" the initiate prefer to call them—but now the government has seen fit to literally sandbag them into oblivion.

As a result of one voluminous set of rule making the Coast Guard has promulgated under the all-encompassing Federal Boat Safety Act, most of the neatly stacked sets of frame patterns for small boats that hang from Eddie England's shop's ceiling won't be moved again.

England, who has been making the little wooden boats since 1930 (they can best be described, perhaps, as exquisite) said he would rather quit the boat building business than get involved in this mess.

England told us what the Coast Guard's new capacity and flotation regulations have done to him during an interview in his neat little work shop on the road to Plum Island last week.

The shop is practically devoid of boat boards, as he calls the special lumber used for his little boats, and though the conversation was punctuated by bits of laughter, it was all rather sad.

England wasn't overly critical of the Coast Guard, saying he realized it had a problem because 574 people died when small boats capsized last year, and it was the major single cause of boating fatalities throughout the country

NEW FEDERAL LAWS regulating stability of mass-produced small craft are sounding death knell for boats of traditional design, such as rowing skiffs by Eddie England, shown in his workshop, with the last two he will build. England is quitting rather than adjust his products.
(PHIL PRESTON photo)

Dear Pink House,

You are a celebrity,
Darling.

Nesting season

It's nesting season
Each egg
Each chick
Each adult
Vital to recovery

The Plight of the
Piping Plover

Plum Island Lookout

No. 3. Vol. 1.   Plum Island Beach, Wednesday, September 5, 1923

BURRIED TREASURE ON PLUM ISLAND BEACH

It is a very old tale that is related of Plum Island and a very interesting one to those who are out for get-rich-quick opportunities. It seems that during the Revolutionary War a chest of silver was taken from the British enemies in nearby towns and burned—very deeply— beneath the shining sands of Plum Island. Of course, there must have been a map showing the exact location of the hidden treasure, but it seems unfortunately to have been misplaced in the years that have passed since the chest was lowered into its sandy grave.

Newburyport citizens, however, are very sure that they know the approximate location of this wealth to be somewhere near the present site of the Plum Island Beach Company's Office. So, if any of the Island vacationists have alittle leisure, a surplus amount of energy, a stout shovel, and a strong faith in the legend, let them begin the search; but let them also remember not to allow their enthusiasm to prompt them to dig the road in search of wealth. Folks who knew Plum Island in its old board walk days prize the road more than many chests of British treasure.

CAPTAIN MADDOCK

TO REMAIN ALL YEAR

MANY VISITORS FLOCK TO ISLAND FOR GALA WEEK

Carnival Week at the Plum Island Beach pavilion promises to be a huge success. Opening formally on Monday evening with a favor party and continuing with a novel attraction each night, the week promises to be one of the most memorable in the history of Plum Island.

Visitors are flocking to the Beach for this celebration, and many of the Beach residents are p rolonging their stay here in order to participate in the festivities.

The program for the week as already announced in the Lookout reads as follows:

Monday, Sept. 3rd: Gala Night—novelty favor party.

Tuesday: Battle of Music between Smithies orchestra of Haverhill and Chickie Burkes' orchestra of Amesbury.

Wednesday: Prize Waltz competition and exhibition dancing by Mr. Roland Ricker.

Thursday: Costume Ball and exhibition dancing by Godfrey Torrey of Newburyport.

Friday: Selection of Miss Plum Island and exhibition dancing by Miss Sally Deicie.

Those who have attended the Pavilion during Carnival Week in previous years look forward to the event with keen interest as the week has

Old tales

I'm a chest of silver
Buried very deeply
In a sandy grave
Beneath the shining sands
Of Plum Island

Find me.
Get rich quick!

run the Busses to the Island through the month of October. As many of the cottages on the Island remain

years of age and increasing in size and age until towards the end of the column came the oldest of the children who were under twelve

included Mrs. Alfred George Horton, Miss Mrs. Maude Bridge,

Parker River National Wildlife Refuge

To the Birds and Threatened Species,

Feed

Fly

Rest

Raise your babies

You are safe on the refuge

Where wildlife comes first

Parker River

NATIONAL WILDLIFE REFUGE

U.S. Fish and Wildlife Service
Department of the Interior

Visitor Center and Headquarters

OPEN

Salt Pannes
Wildlife Observation
Area
↗
Live Parking Only

Quiet waters of the salt marsh

I flood quietly
Into the salt marsh

Then I pull back
To the sea

Life in the salt marsh
Depends on me

I am the tide.

Rowboats

Anchored rowboats
Rest
In the basin

Saltmarsh sparrow

Saltmarsh Sparrow
Shifts on the eggs in her nest

The moon is filling
The tide will rise
The marsh will flood
Where the nest is nestled

Saltmarsh Sparrow
Must leave her nest

And wait
For the waters to ebb

Then fledge her chicks
Before the tides return
In ten days

Treasures

The tide sweeps away
And back again

Revealing treasures
Then hiding them

Sometimes the treasures
Stay ashore
When the waves rush them in

Under the sea

Barnacled tales
Blowholes
And fins

Peeking up

From
Under

The
Sea

Vessels and vehicles for rescue

Launching the Lifeboat, Plum Island, Newburyport, Mass.

In the height of the storm
Life saving crews
To the rescue!

Walking to school from Plum Island

Four and a half miles
Each way
In one day

Trudging a path
In the snow

A STURDY LAD FROM PLUM ISLAND

Arthur Woods Walks From the Point to Jackman School.

Arthur Woods, Jr., the 13-year-old son of Arthur Woods, lighthouse keeper at Plum Island, is so desirous of an education that distance has no terrors for him. Monday he walked from Plum Island point to the Jackman school in this city, where he is a student, and in spite of the bitter cold and high wind he was on hand again yesterday.

From Plum Island point to the Jackman is about four and a half miles, and in addition to trudging that distance along a rough path in the snow the plucky young fellow has to repeat the journey in order to reach his home, making a round trip of nine miles that he proposes to do daily in order that he may have the privilege of attending school.

When the weather is propitious and the cars running he will be able to get a lift part of the way, but as there is little likelihood of the cars going beyond Ocean avenue until the snow disappears it can readily be seen that he is in for some great tramping before the winter is over.

The lad is rugged and determined and seems to think that he can conquer the difficulties successfully, as he prefers the exercise, with an opportunity of living at home, to living in the city and away from home.

Xtra extra read all about it!

Joyful youngsters
Play all day
On the clean sands
Of Plum Island

PLUM ISLAND BEACH

The Children's Paradise

Nothing that we can say about Plum Island Beach could be half as eloquent as the great, big unqualified endorsement that the hundreds of joyful youngsters registered at the Children's Carnival last Saurday.

The Mothers and Daddies who bring their little ones here from nearby and distant places in preference to all other places, because here they gain in health and strength, summer after summer, were as happy as the children. The sight of those little robust figures, each radiating health and happiness was proof of their wisdom in selecting a summer home here and of course they were proud of such splendid children.

Nowhere could Mothers be so free from care as here. They just turn the children loose without a worry knowing that they are perfectly safe and will return when hungry. They are not brought into contact with those undesirable elements or enterprises which tend to influence the child's mind unfavorably. Here you put them in a bathing suit or rompers in the morning and they play all day in the clean sand or on the shores of the Basin with dozens of others. There are no commercial enterprises here calling for a stream of nickles and dimes.

We owe it to our children to endow them in their youth with healthy bodies and clean minds and to cultivate self-reliance and confidence. Conditions at Plum Island help to attain this end.

We make it possible for the head of a family by the exercise of a little thrift to acquire a summer home on Plum Island Beach.

Lots are sold as low as $350. on the most easy terms. Only ten per cent. down and the balance in monthly payments. No taxes or interest to pay, non-forfeiture of money already paid if in case of curtailment of purchaser's income, payments of installments are delayed. Free deeds are given to family in case of death of purchaser before payments are completed.

Sensible restrictions against undesirable amusement enterprises and building regulations which insure ample room surrounding all buildings and prevent crowding, will preserve those conditions which make Plum Island Beach so attractive.

It you want your children to enjoy equal opportunity for health and happiness with the children of others

GET YOUR LOT NOW - - BUILD ANYTIME

Plum Island Beach Company

Yellow warbler

Sing to us
The song
Of bright yellow
Sunshine

Zigzagging boardwalks

Some boardwalks
Zigzag
Through the trees

Some boardwalks
Zigzag
Through the dunes

Some boardwalks
Send you to the skies
Above **Plum Island**

Take a Scavenger Hunt through the list below to learn more!

Some poems are found poems that include exact words and phrases from the following:

A   Displays at Burgess Aviation Museum

B   "Habitats of a Barrier Island," a display at the Parker
River National Wildlife Refuge

C   The pamphlet called, "Frequently Asked Questions: Massachusetts Marine Fisheries Shellfish Purification Plant" by David E. Pierce, PhD, Director (November 2015). Pamphlet given out at the Plant.

H   Signs at the Hellcat Wildlife Observation Area

K   Phrases from the description of Keeper Phineas George at the time of his retirement in 1857, as noted on the following website: http://lighthousefriends.com/light.asp?ID=651

M   For boat shop: the newspaper article pictured

N   The video, "This Beach is for the Birds" playing at the Parker River National Wildlife Refuge Visitor Center

O   Article pictured

P   Displays at the Hellcat Wildlife Observation Area, including the sign, "Welcome to Parker River National Wildlife Refuge"

S   Newburyport Daily News column by saltmarsh ecologist, David Samuel Johnson:
http://www.newburyportnews.com/news/local_news/great-marsh-sparrows-a-harbinger-for-things-to-come/article_ab33eb33-00ee-5ba6-959e-7191af8ef998.html
This is also a blog entry on his science and writing blog: https://manayunkia.wordpress.com/science-writing/

V   Newspaper article from long ago (Investigate what vehicles are used today!)

W   Newspaper article pictured, "A Sturdy Lad from Plum Island" (1910)

X   Newspaper article pictured, "Plum Island Beach: The Children's Paradise" (1923)

Some poems do not use exact words and phrases from other places; ideas came from:

D   The diary of Plum Island Lighthouse Keeper Arthur W. Woods, Sr. in the year 1911 (select entries pictured). It is believed that Keeper Woods, his wife Emma Grace Woods, and his daughter, E. Grace Woods wrote entries. It is not clear if his son, Arthur W. Woods, Jr. wrote entries or not.

E   The photographs for letters B and E, taken the day after a coastal storm in March of 2013. PITA sponsored flights document the erosion of the shoreline.

F   A visit to Surfland Bait and Tackle; pictured are lures sold at the shop

J   Walking the boardwalk and talking with a local swimmer
(Pictured: Craig Filmore)

L   A visit to the Plum Island Lighthouse

M   For The Pink House: Viewing artwork inspired by The Pink House and readings that include its history and present-day passion for this iconic landmark

Q   The presentation, "Plum Island in a Changing Climate: Vulnerability, Science, and Adaptation" given by Wildlife biologist, Nancy Pau and partners, on June 25, 2018 at the Parker River Wildlife Refuge Visitor Center

Y   Display at the Parker River Wildlife Refuge Visitor Center

Z   Inspired by the current boardwalk replacement project for Hellcat Trail. This trail will become accessible for people of all abilities, in line with the Americans with Disabilities Act of 1990 and standards for accessible design. Also, visit the Friends of Parker River National Wildlife Refuge at https://parkerriver.org to learn about the engraved planks that will improve the safety of all boardwalks on the refuge!